Alien
Raid

Steve Barlow and Steve Skidmore
Illustrated by Sonia Leong

LONDON·SYDNEY

First published in 2011
by Franklin Watts

Text © Steve Barlow and Steve Skidmore 2011
Illustrations © Sonia Leong 2011
Cover design by Jonathan Hair

Franklin Watts
338 Euston Road
London NW1 3BH

Franklin Watts Australia
Level 17/207 Kent Street
Sydney, NSW 2000

A CIP catalogue record for this book
is available from the British Library.

ISBN: 978 1 4451 0267 2

1 3 5 7 9 10 8 6 4 2

Printed in Great Britain

Franklin Watts is a division of Hachette Children's Books,
an Hachette UK company.
www.hachette.co.uk

ABOUT THE 2STEVES

Steve Barlow was born in Crewe, in the UK, and has worked at various times as a teacher, an actor, a stage manager and a puppeteer in England, and in Botswana, Africa. He met Steve Skidmore at a school in Nottingham and the 2Steves began writing together. Steve Barlow now lives in Somerset and sails a boat named Which Way, so called because he usually hasn't a clue where he's going.

Steve Skidmore is shorter and less hairy than Steve Barlow. After passing some exams at school, he went on to Nottingham University where he spent most of his time playing sport and doing a variety of heroic summer jobs, including counting pastry pie lids (honest). He trained as a teacher of Drama, English and Film Studies, before teaming up with Steve Barlow to become a full-time author.

Together they have written many books, including:
Crime Team and iHorror
Find out more at:
www.the2steves.net

ABOUT THE ILLUSTRATOR

Sonia Leong is based in Cambridge, in the UK, and is a super-star manga artist. She won Tokyopop's first UK Rising Stars of Manga competition (2005–06) and her first graphic novel was Manga Shakespeare: Romeo and Juliet. She's a member of Sweatdrop Studios and has too many awards to fit in this teeny space.
Find Sonia at her website: www.fyredrake.net

Decide your own destiny...

This book is not like others you may have read. You are the hero of this adventure. It is up to you to make decisions that will affect how the adventure unfolds.

Each section of this book is numbered. At the end of most sections, you will have to make a choice. The choice you make will take you to a different section of the book.

Some of your choices will help you to complete the adventure successfully. But choose carefully, some of your decisions could be fatal!

If you fail, then start the adventure again and learn from your mistake.

If you choose correctly you will succeed in your adventure.

Don't be a zero, be a hero!

It is the year 2150. You are a top Flight Commander in the Galaxy Defence Force (GDF). You have taken part in hundreds of dangerous missions for the GDF. You have also fought in many battles against hostile alien life forms, who wish to conquer Earth.

You and your Flight Squadron are based on the GDF base on the planet Mars. It is Earth's forward defence against any alien attacks. If you fail to defeat the enemy forces, then Earth would be doomed.

You are asleep in your dorm pod, when you are awoken by an alarm. A computer voice screams out. "Code Alpha Alert! Code Alpha Alert!"

You snap awake. Code Alpha is the alert signal for an alien attack! You jump out of your bed, pull on your combat uniform and head to the base control centre.

Now go to section 1.

1

At the base control centre, General Drake, your commanding officer, is grim faced.

"We have a problem," she says. "Intelligence satellites have picked up signs of an alien fleet heading towards Earth."

"Is it hostile?" you ask.

"We sent up drone interceptors, based on Neptune, but they have been attacked and destroyed. They were taken out with high energy lasers."

"How far away is this fleet?" you say.

"Our computers calculate that it will be here within two hours," replies General Drake. "We're the last line of defence against this invasion! What do you think we should do?"

To contact the alien force, go to 8.
To attack the aliens straight away, go to 36.
To find out more about the aliens, go to 48.

2

You take out the BHG, but as you do more lasers spring out from the wall. A stream of energy bolts hits you and you fall to the floor.

The BHG spins out of your grasp.

"Too late, Earthling!" laughs the Nagga commander. Another bolt hits you before you can move, and your life fades away.

You came so far, but still failed. To begin again, go to 1.

3

The decoy force is launched. You know the robot ships won't be coming back, but they will give you time to get to the Nagga mother ship.

Then it's your turn to blast off. Flying in stealth mode, you and the squadron set your course to the extreme right of the Nagga fleet. You hope you will take the enemy by surprise.

Suddenly a single dot appears on the scanner screen. You realise that it must be a Nagga scout ship.

If you wish to avoid the ship, go to 14.
If you wish to attack it, go to 31.

4

Guided by the robo suit's navigation system, you arrive at the emergency exit.

To your horror you see that it is locked.

To blast your way in, go to 26.

To head to the service chute on Level 10, go to 21.

To head to the docking port on Level 7, go to 44.

5

You take out the BHG and hide it under the dead Nagga commander. You set it to detonate in fifteen minutes. This will give you a chance to get off the ship, but you still risk being sucked into the black hole.

Quickly, your robo suit guides you off the ship. You reach the emergency exit – there are only two minutes left! You blast open the door. You know too much time has passed. You will not be able to get far enough away from the ship, but you launch yourself into the blackness of space, waiting for the explosion…

Go to 50.

6

You take out your blaster and pull the trigger. In a flash of light, the droid explodes into thousands of pieces.

You know you have little time before the Naggas come hunting for you. "Scan mother ship," you order your robo suit. Its navigation system projects a hologram of the ship. You identify the ship's reactor room and the control deck.

If you wish to head to the reactor room, go to 19.

If you wish to head to the control deck, go to 11.

7

You and your support fighters swing away from the fight, heading towards the rear of the Nagga mother ship. Nagga fighters still pester you, but these are dealt with quickly.

Nazeema's voice comes through the comm link. "I don't suppose there is a secret weak spot so we can fire a neutron rocket into the heart of the ship and blow it up?"

You laugh. "What do you think this is, a movie? Who would design a ship like that?"

"So what's the plan?" she asks.

To attack the mother ship, go to 22.
To find out more about the ship, go to 46.

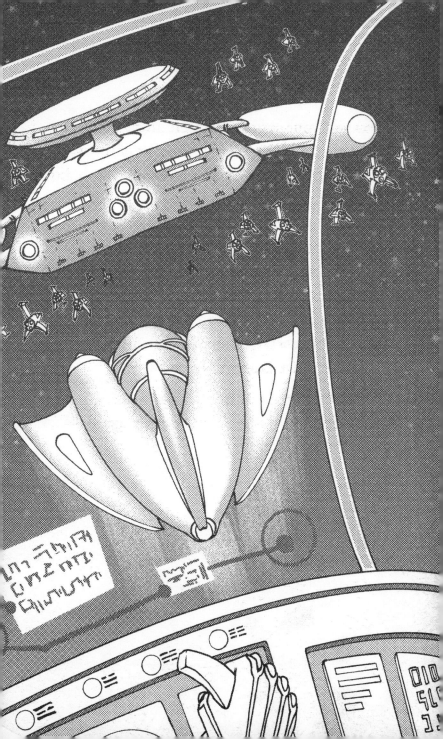

8

"I think we should contact the aliens and find out if they are hostile, before we attack. We don't want to cause a diplomatic incident."

General Drake scowls. "You're sure?"

"Yes," you nod.

"Very well, I just hope you're right. Computer, transmit message. Use all known frequencies."

You begin your message. "GDF Mars base speaking to alien fleet, please identify yourself. Where are you from and what are your intentions?"

Ten minutes later, an alien face appears on the comm link screen.

"GDF, we come in peace, we come in peace. We wish to hold friendly talks with you and your leaders…"

The screen goes blank.

"Signal lost," says the computer.

If you believe the alien, go to 25.

If you wish to fly and attack the fleet, go to 36.

If you wish to find out more about the aliens, go to 48.

9

You fly at the fighter, firing mini-missiles from your arm launchers. They hit the enemy and it explodes.

However, by attacking the ship, you have given away your position!

Heavy weapons fire at you from the mother ship. Clouds of missiles and plasma bolts blast towards you. A missile hits you, and it's all over.

If you want to be a hero, you can start the mission again by going back to 1.

10

You fly your ultra fighter into the swarm of enemy spacecraft, taking out several with plasma rockets.

Your computer's voice warns you of an incoming missile and you spin away, just avoiding it. There is an explosion to your left – one of your squadron has been hit. More Nagga fighters appear and you realise you are badly outnumbered!

If you wish to break off the attack, go to 18.

If you want to continue the fight, go to 23.

If you wish to try to get to the mother ship, go to 38.

11

You head towards the control deck. Your nav systems help you to avoid any Nagga guards, warning you when any approach. The droids that come your way are less fortunate – you blast them into pieces before they know what's hit them.

You finally reach the control deck. The door is guarded by several Nagga guards.

If you wish to step forward and shoot the guards, go to 34.

If you wish to attack with grenades, go to 41.

If you wish to go to the reactor room instead, go to 19.

12

"I'll take the attack drone," you say.

"I will load it," replies the service robot.

You call your squadron together and brief them on the Nagga fleet. "You know we are the last line of defence," you tell them. "If this fleet gets past us, then Earth is doomed. We have to take out the mother ship. Any questions?"

"What's the plan of attack?" asks Nazeema, your second-in-command.

If you want to attack the Nagga, go to 33.

To send a robot force to distract the Nagga fleet, go to 39.

13

The lift shoots downwards before coming to a sudden stop. The doors swoosh open revealing a row of heavily armed Nagga guards, all pointing their weapons at you.

"Prisoner delivery," says the droid. "Take him to the cells."

You have been tricked!

If you wish to surrender, go to 47.

If you wish to fight, go to 32.

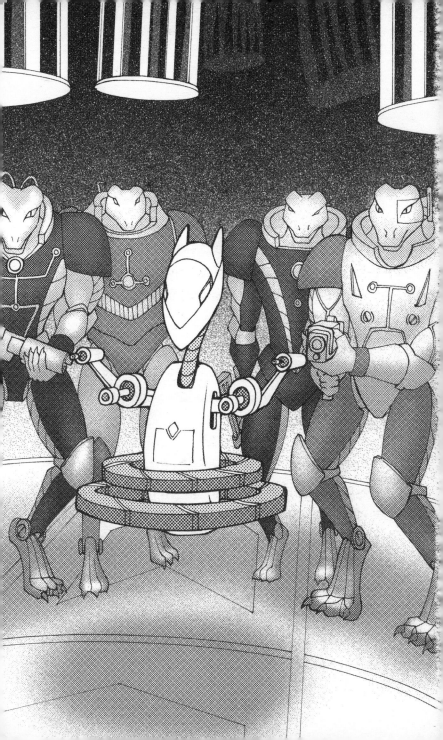

14

"Remain in stealth mode. Do not attack," you tell the others. "We don't want to give away our position."

The Nagga scout ship passes out of range and you remain undetected.

"Continue on course to the mother ship," you tell the squadron.

Twenty minutes later you are within range of the main Nagga fleet.

If you wish to attack the Nagga as a full squadron, go to 49.

If you want to split the squadron into two, go to 38.

15

"Stealth mode," you tell the robo suit.

You breathe a sigh of relief as you fly unseen past the Nagga fighter and head towards your target.

You call up the plans of the mother ship: there are three entry points.

If you want to head to a service chute on Level 10, go to 21.

If you want to head to an emergency exit on Level 9, go to 4.

If you want to head to a docking port on Level 7, go to 44.

16

"Evasive action," you order your flight computer.

Your ultra fighter spins around, climbing and diving. There are too many enemy fighters and they move in for the kill. The blackness around you is lit up as streams of plasma bolts streak past you.

You switch to manual flight to try to evade the incoming fire, but it is impossible. The last sight you see is a flash of orange as the plasma bolts rip your ultra fighter apart.

You have failed. Earth is at the mercy of the aliens.

If you wish to begin again, go to 1.

17

You hide the BHG and your blaster in your suit's leg compartment.

You speak and your robo suit translates for you. "I am a rebel soldier. I have come to offer my services to the Nagga. I have information that will be of interest to your leader."

The droid scans you. After a few seconds it replies, "Come with me."

If you wish to go with the droid, go to 28.
If you don't want to, go to 43.

18

"Retreat!" you order. You spin your ultra fighter away from the enemy, but it is too late! Streams of Nagga missiles head towards you.

"Incoming! Incoming!" warns your computer.

It is the last thing you hear as a missile hits your fighter and engulfs it in a fireball.

You have failed. If you wish to begin again, go to 1.

19

You head towards the reactor room. You come across a couple of groups of Nagga guards, but your weapons systems easily blast them out of the way.

Finally you reach the reactor room.

You blast open the door and step inside.

It is the last thing you ever do! A wave of radioactivity surges out, frying you to a crisp!

You have paid the ultimate price.

To start your mission again, go to 1.

20

You pick up the BHG. "Call all space pilots to action stations," you tell the computer. "Code Alpha – immediate launch." The computer obeys.

"Good luck," says the General.

"I think we're going to need it," you reply.

You make your way to the hangars, where your ultra fighters are being prepared for launch by the service robots.

The Chief Service Robot flies towards you. "Commander, I have armed your fighter with lasers and plasma rockets, but which payload do you wish to take – an attack drone or your robotic flying suit?

If you want to take the robo suit, go to 45.

If you wish to take the attack drone, go to 12.

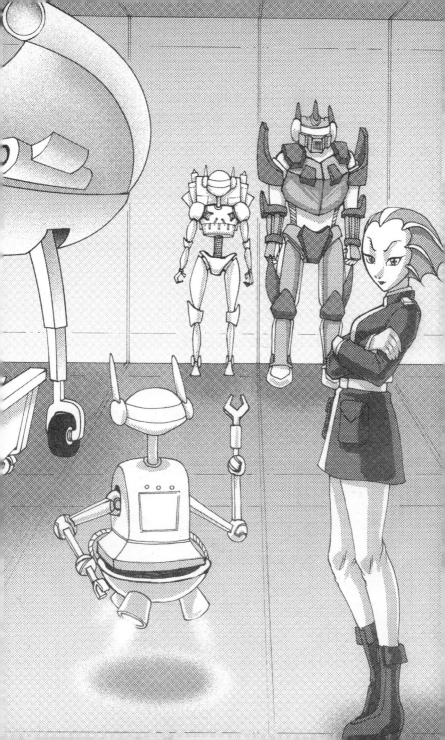

21

Guided by the robo suit's navigation system, you arrive at the service chute. It is open and you fly into the heart of the Nagga mother ship.

Soon you are standing in a large service bay. In front of you are several Nagga fighters, which are being serviced by crews of drones and repair robots.

A sentry droid hovers over to you. It speaks to you and your robo suit translates its words. "Unknown life form. Identify yourself."

If you want to try to trick the droid, go to 17.

If you wish to attack the droid, go to 43.

22

"We need to attack the mother ship," you say.

"That'll be a suicide mission," says Nazeema.

"I wasn't thinking of flying straight at it," you reply. "I've got a plan."

If you chose to bring the attack drone, go to 40.

If you chose the robo suit, go to 35.

23

"Attack with full force!" you shout into your comm link. Your squadron takes an attack pattern to meet the Nagga star fighters head on.

The air is filled with missiles, plasma bolts and flashes of laser fire. Explosions rock your fighter as both sides take casualties. As you blast an enemy fighter to pieces, you see Nazeema's ship come under attack from a Nagga fighter.

At that same moment your computer's voice fills your ears. "Incoming fighters!" You glance left and see several Nagga star fighters heading towards you.

If you wish to take evasive action, go to 16.
If you wish to help Nazeema, go to 27.

24

You don't know how to steer the ship, so you blast the control panels. But it's no use – the ship carries on moving towards Earth.

You do not see the Nagga guards enter the control deck. They shoot you in the back with their lasers and you slump down dead.

To try to save Earth once again, go to 1.

25

"I think we should listen to what the aliens have to say," you tell General Drake.

She hesitates. "Are you sure?"

You nod. "Computer, try opening a comms link. Send a greeting message."

The computer transmits the greeting message, but there is no reply.

Suddenly, an alarm screeches again. "Code Alpha!" Before you can react, the base is rocked by a series of explosions. The alien fleet is attacking!

You look at the vid screen.

"How have they got here so quickly?" shouts General Drake. You have no answer. "I shouldn't have listened to you," screams Drake. "Launch all ultra fighters!"

But before you can react, an energy bomb hits the control centre. A fireball engulfs the room. You pass into blackness, knowing that Earth is doomed.

To begin the mission again, go to 1.

26

You aim your suit's energy blaster and open fire at the door.

You are horrified as the weapon has no effect. You realise that the door is protected by an energy shield! But there is worse to come. Lasers suddenly spring out from the mother ship and point at you.

You try to turn, but it is too late. The lasers open fire and streams of energy bolts pulse out, ripping you and your suit apart.

You have paid the ultimate price. To begin again, go to 1.

27

You thrust your controls forward and accelerate towards Nazeema's attacker.

You fire your lasers. One of the Nagga fighters disappears in a ball of flame. You fire again, but there are too many enemy ships. You give a cry as Nazeema's ultra fighter is hit by a missile and is vaporised.

It is the last thing you see as another enemy missile hits your ship and you too are disintegrated.

If you wish to begin again, turn to 1.

28

You follow the droid out of the service bay, keeping a careful distance.

You travel through long metallic corridors, passing many Nagga guards and droids. They take little notice of you.

Eventually, the droid stops. You look around – there is no one else about. A lift door opens. "Get in," the droid orders.

If you wish to obey the droid, go to 13.
If you want to attack it, go to 6.

29

"The Nagga have stealth technology which makes their ships hard to detect. We need to see what we're up against."

General Drake nods. "Good decision."

"Run all light, sound and thermal scans we have," you tell the computers.

Within minutes an image appears on the vid screen.

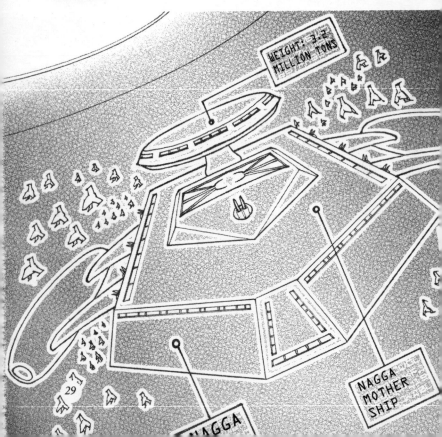

WEIGHT: 3.2 MILLION TONS

NAGGA MOTHER SHIP

NAGGA

You stare at the screen. "That mother ship is huge! And with the amount of support ships, I think we can safely say that they aren't dropping in for a cup of coffee and a biscuit!"

If you wish to negotiate with the Nagga, go to 25.

If you wish to prepare to attack the Nagga fleet, go to 42.

30

You continue to fight, but the odds are overwhelming. You let loose a continuous stream of mini-missiles and blaster fire, destroying several of your attackers.

The bay is filled with explosions and fireballs. You fight desperately, but you know you are doomed.

A Nagga guard sneaks up behind you. He blasts you in the back and you crash forwards. The Nagga quickly close in and tear you and your robo suit apart.

You have failed to save the Earth. If you wish to try again, go to 1.

31

"Squadron, I am engaging the enemy," you say.

You switch on your weapons system and target the Nagga scout ship.

"Fire," you order the computer.

A volley of mini-missiles hits the Nagga ship and it is vaporised.

Seconds later you realise that you have made a big mistake as your scanner screen fills with dozens of white dots heading towards you at high speed. By attacking the scout ship, you have given away your position to the enemy!

Nagga star fighters loom ahead of you. You are in trouble!

To take evasive action, go to 16.
To attack the Nagga fighters, go to 23.

32

You grab your blaster and begin firing laser bolts at the Naggas.

You kick the security droid out of the lift and shoot it. The droid explodes and takes out several of the Nagga guards. You finish them off with a burst of fire from your blaster.

"Scan mother ship," you order your robo suit. A hologram of the ship is projected from your navigation system.

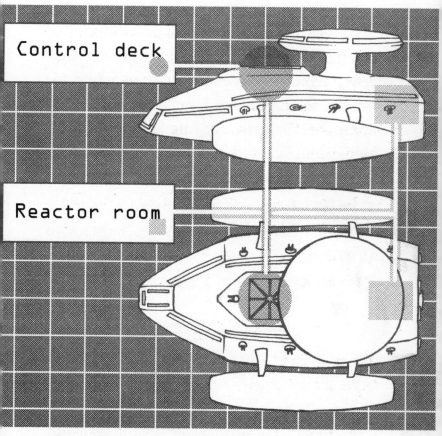

To head to the control deck, go to 11.
To head to the reactor room, go to 19.

33

"We will attack them head on," you tell your squadron. "Use your comm links to keep in contact. Fly well and fight hard."

Soon your squadron has launched and you are heading through the blackness of space towards the Nagga fleet. You pass Jupiter and are travelling towards the moons of Saturn...

"Enemy ships ahead," warns the flight computer. You glance at your scanner and your stomach turns. Hundreds of white dots are moving towards you at high speed.

If you wish to take evasive action, go to 16.

If you wish to attack the Nagga fighters, go to 23.

34

Before you can move, laser guns spring out, pointing at you. You try to get away, but you are too slow. Streams of laser bolts rip into your body.

If you wish to begin the mission again, go to 1.

35

"I'm going to use the robo suit," you tell Nazeema. "I need you to cover me."

You climb into the robo suit and pick up the BHG bomb. You hit the eject button and shoot out of the fighter. You engage the robo suit's jet packs and fly towards the Nagga mother ship.

Suddenly an enemy fighter appears straight ahead of you.

If you wish to attack the fighter, go to 9.
If you wish to try to avoid it, go to 15.

36

"I don't think we should trust aliens that destroy our drones," you tell General Drake. "We have to attack immediately!"

Within minutes, you and your squadron launch and head towards the alien fleet.

Then, from out of nowhere, dozens of alien fighters appear! They begin to fire at you.

"Break formation!" you shout into your comm link. You take out several enemy ships, but you and your squadron are outnumbered.

Go to 16.

37

You spin out of the way and fire your blaster at the commander. An energy stream hits the creature. You follow this up with a handful of grenades and a volley of mini-missiles.

The creature doesn't stand a chance. Its half-snake, half-machine body is ripped apart.

"End of the game," you say. "I win."

"I do not think so," says the dying Nagga commander. "I have already programmed this ship to destroy your planet. You can't change my mind!" Then the alien dies.

The ship continues on its course and you know you have to stop it. If you use the BHG, it will almost certainly mean death.

If you want to set off the BHG, go to 5.
If you wish to try to stop the mother ship using the ship's controls, go to 24.

38

"Break into two flights," you tell the squadron. "Black flight attack mode. Red flight follow me, we're going to try to get behind the mother ship. Nazeema, keep me covered."

You order your computer to navigate a course behind the Nagga mother ship. Nazeema and three other ultra fighters follow you.

You leave Black flight to attack the enemy ships, knowing that they are fighting for their lives. Explosions light up the blackness as the Nagga fight back.

Go to 7.

39

"There are too many enemy ships to attack head on," you tell the squadron. "We will send out a decoy force of flight robots. The ships will transmit digital decoy signals, to make the Nagga think that they are being attacked by a large force. Meanwhile, the rest of the squadron will fly a longer route. We will use stealth mode until we are in sight of the mother ship. Then we attack it with ultimate force and destroy it!"

Nazeema grins. "A very simple plan, Commander."

You smile. "The best ones are! Let's hope for Earth's sake, it works. To your fighters!"

Go to 3.

40

"I'm sending in the attack drone armed with the Black Hole Generator," you tell Nazeema. "We'll have to get closer before we launch it. Follow me."

The flight heads towards the mother ship. "Computer, prepare to launch drone."

At that moment heavy guns on the mother ship open fire. Streams of plasma bolts and swarms of missiles streak towards you. Dozens of Nagga star fighters appear and attack.

Two of your fighters are blown to pieces. You return fire and take out three enemy ships.

"Launch drone!" you order the computer, but it is too late. A Nagga missile hits your fighter, sending you into oblivion.

You have failed. If you wish to begin your mission again, go to 1.

41

Before the guards can react, you take them out with a couple of energy grenades. Your way to the control deck is clear!

You blast open the door and step inside. What you see amazes you!

"Welcome to my ship," says the Nagga commander. "You did well to get this far, Earthling, but you cannot stop us from destroying your puny planet."

Laser guns suddenly spring from out of the walls. You move quickly and just avoid laser bolts. Again more guns open up at you. You realise that the commander is controlling the ship through his thoughts! If you destroy the commander, you will be able to stop the attack!

If you wish to use the Black Hole Generator, go to 2.

If you wish to attack the Nagga commander, go to 37.

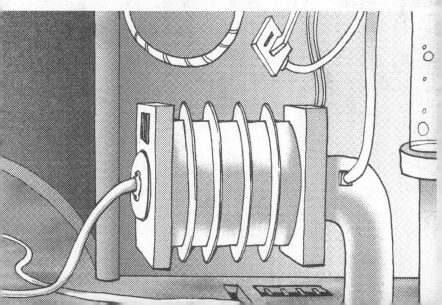

42

"We will have to try to take out the mother ship," you say. "Destroy that and the other ships will be helpless."

General Drake nods. "I think you'll need something to help you." She opens up a secure locker and takes out a small black box.

"What's this?" you ask.

"It's a brand-new, top-secret weapon. It's the most deadly weapon we have. It's a BHG – a Black Hole Generator. A smart bomb creates a mini black hole," explains Drake. "When it is set off, it forms a gravity field, like a black hole, which will suck in anything that is near to it. It is a weapon of last resort. If you are too close to it when it explodes, you'll be sucked into the black hole as well."

"I hope we won't need it," you reply.

Go to 20.

43

You grab your blaster and blow the droid to pieces. But you realise this is a mistake as alarms begin to wail.

Doors slide open and dozens of Nagga guards appear, shooting at you. The service bay is filled with the light and sound of energy weapons.

You fire back with your blaster, and launch a stream of mini-missiles. Explosions rip through the bay as equipment ignites. But you are hopelessly outnumbered!

If you wish to try to get out of the bay, go to 34.

If you wish to continue to fight, go to 30.

44

Guided by the robo suit's navigation system, you arrive at the docking port.

To your horror you see it is shut.

If you wish to blast your way in, go to 26.

If you want to try to find a different way in, go to 34.

45

"I'll take the robo suit," you say. "I may have to use it to get into the Nagga's mother ship."

"A good choice, Commander," replies the service robot. "I will load it immediately."

You call your squadron together and brief them on the Nagga fleet. "You all know that we are the last line of defence," you tell them. "If we fail, then Earth is doomed. We have to take out the mother ship. Any questions?"

"What is the plan of attack?" asks Nazeema, your second-in-command.

To attack the Nagga directly, go to 33.
To send a decoy robot force, go to 39.

46

"We need intelligence on the mother ship," you tell Nazeema.

"Scan the enemy ship," you tell the computer. "Check for points of entry."

Within seconds a holographic image of the ship appears on your screen.

"Find the weakest point of entry," you tell the computer.

The computer replies, "Weakest point is a service chute on Level Ten." An image of the entrance comes up on the screen.

That's the way in, you think.

If you chose to bring the attack drone, go to 40.

If you chose the robo suit, go to 35.

47

You raise your arms. "OK, you got me," you say.

The Nagga guards strip you of your robo suit and weapons. Then you are thrown into a dark metal cell. There is no escape. The Earth is doomed.

If you wish to begin again, go to 1.

48

"I think we need to find out more about our visitors," you tell General Drake.

She nods. "Activate the outer solar system intelligence scanners."

Soon data is pouring back to the GDF base and being analysed by computer BOTS. One of the machines hands you a report.

```
ALIEN RACE:    NAGGA
HOME PLANET:   KADRUN
STATUS:        HOSTILE
TECHNOLOGY:    ADVANCED


- HIGH POWER WEAPONS
INCLUDING STAR FIGHTERS
ARMED WITH LASER CANNONS
AND MISSILE LAUNCHERS.
- STEALTH TECHNOLOGY
WHICH CAN HIDE THEIR
SHIPS IN SPACE.
```

You give a whistle. "The Nagga are snakelike creatures. Not nice…"

"What do you think we should do?" asks Drake.

If you want to talk to the Nagga, go to 25.
If you want more information about their fleet, go to 29.

49

"Attack mode!" you order.

The squadron respond. You head towards the Nagga fleet, lasers blazing and missiles firing. You have surprised the Nagga and your squadron take out several enemy ships. But the Nagga respond and soon dozens of star fighters are attacking you.

You fly your ultra fighter through the raging battle. Ahead of you is the Nagga mother ship – it is huge!

If you want to try to get to the mother ship, go to 38.
If you wish to continue fighting, go to 10.
If you wish to break off the attack, go to 18.

50

"Need a lift, Commander?" You hear Nazeema's voice in your comm link.

You glance to your right and see her ultra fighter. You head towards it and attach yourself to it with the robo suit's magnetic clamps.

"Get us out of here!" you shout.

The next few seconds are a blur as Nazeema's fighter speeds away from the Nagga mother ship.

Then there is a huge ripple that shakes your bones. Shock waves send Nazeema's fighter spinning. Then there is total darkness as the mini black hole is formed. It begins to suck you back as gravity takes over and drags the mother ship and the Nagga fighters into its depths.

For a second you are also pulled back, but the ultra fighter breaks free and blasts away!

"That was close," laughs Nazeema. "Hang on, we're going home! You've saved the Earth – you're a total hero!"

ARTIST AT WORK!

Hi there! I'm Sonia, and I draw all the artwork in the I HERO books. I work mainly as a manga artist and I run drawing workshops, too.

I draw in three main stages for I HERO. First, I sketch out the rough positions in pencil. Then I make any changes and work up the art in ink. Finally, I add layers of texture for the fills and shadows.

This is the art from section 5. I changed the final piece to show more of the Nagga commander, and also to alter the position of the robo suit hand.

This is what happens when the instructions to me aren't very clear. It was only after I'd drawn this droid for section 20 that I realised it was supposed to hover. I made the change in the final piece below, so it was easy to fix, but it's another reason why it's important to draw roughs first.

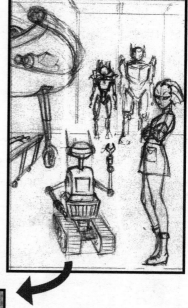

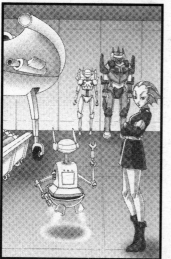

Want the chance to see your I HERO fan art* in an I HERO book? Send it to:

**I HERO fan art
EDGE/Franklin Watts
15th Floor, 338 Euston Road,
London NW1 3BH**

or email it to:

ad@hachettechildrens.co.uk

*Sorry, but we won't be able to return any art to you – so take a photo of it first!
Write your name, age and address on each piece of fan art.

Castle
of Doom

Steve Barlow and Steve Skidmore
Illustrated by Sonia Leong

You are the last of the great warrior wizards,
living in a world of magic and monsters. Your
skill as a wizard is only matched by your skills
in sword fighting.

Many different types of creature live in your
world. Goblins, trolls and dwarves live side by
side with men and women.

It is the time of Midwinter and you are at
home, eating a hearty supper and reading an
old book of spells in front of a roaring fire. As
you read of ancient spells to defeat demons
there is a loud and desperate knocking at the
door. You know at once that someone needs
your help…

Continue reading the adventure in
I HERO Castle of Doom

I HERO
DECIDE YOUR OWN DESTINY
Castle of Doom
EDGE
Steve Barlow - Steve Skidmore

Want to read more "You Are The Hero" adventures? Well, why not try these...

Also by the 2Steves: iHorror
Fight your fear. Choose your fate.

978 1 40830 985 8 pb
978 1 40831 476 0 eBook

978 1 40830 986 5 pb
978 1 40831 477 7 eBook

978 1 40830 988 9 pb
978 1 40831 479 1 eBook

978 1 40830 987 2 pb
978 1 40831 478 4 eBook